© D.C. Thomson & Co., Ltd 2000

Published 2000 by BEANObooks geddes&grosset ,
an imprint of Children's Leisure Products Limited,
David Dale House, New Lanark ML11 9DJ, Scotland

ISBN 1 84205 032 X

Printed and bound in Scotland

COPS 'n' ROBBERS

BEANO**books**
geddes & grosset

A gorilla trap set by the clever Sid chap!

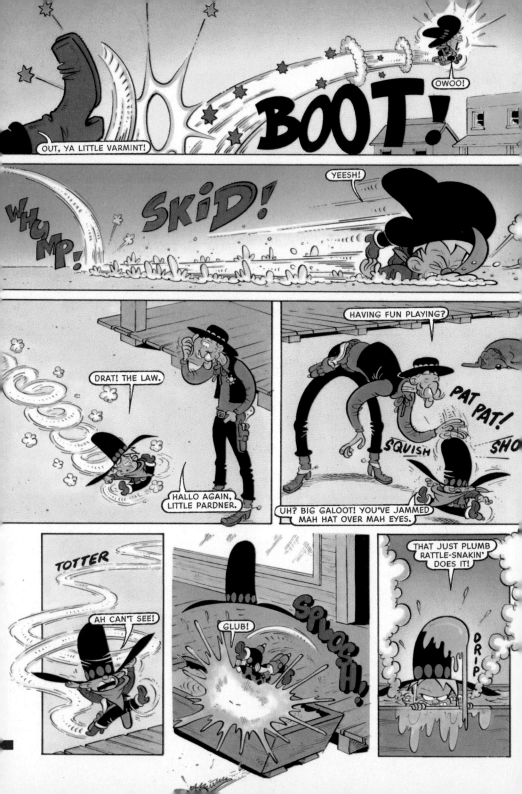

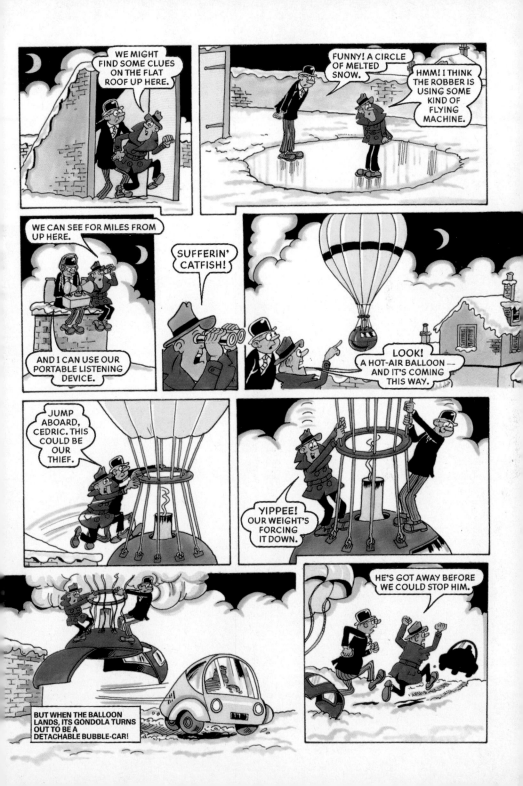

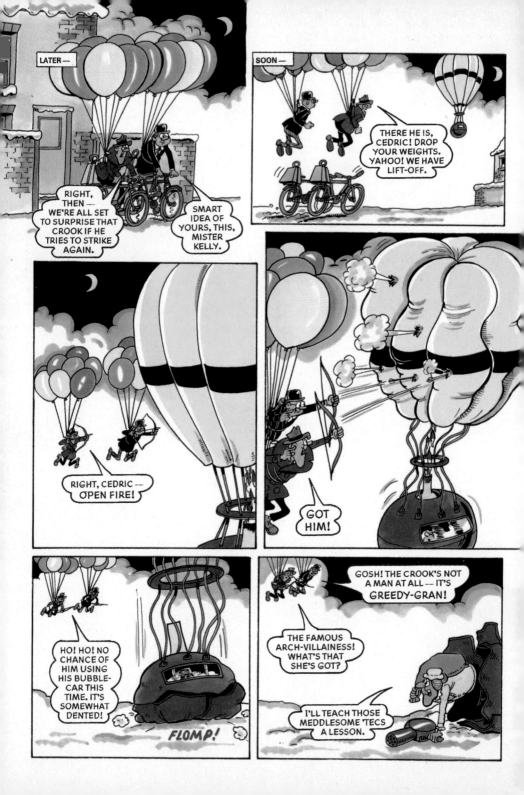

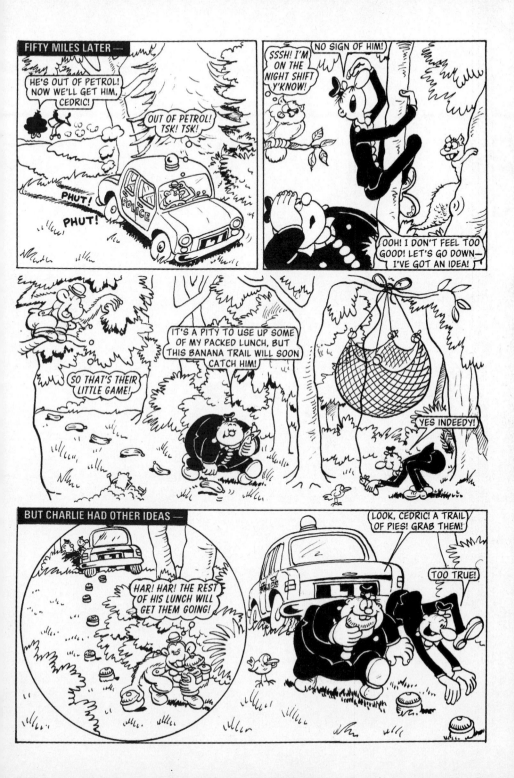

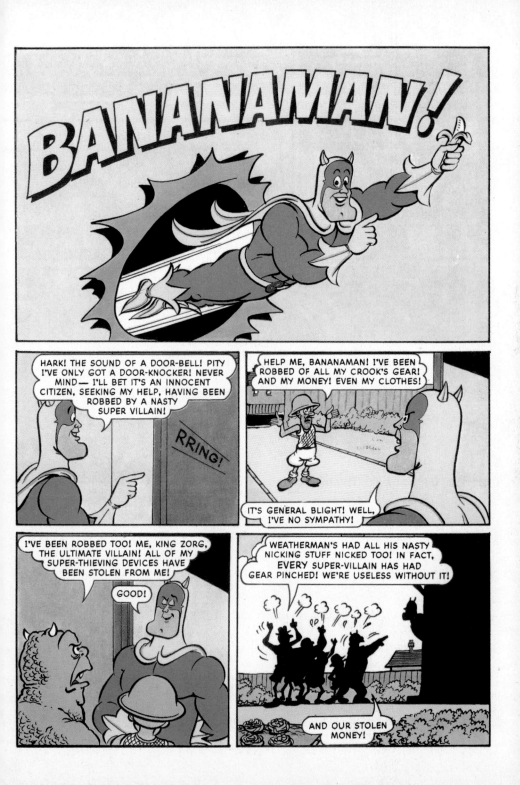